Praise for
Voices Unheard: A Reflective Journal

"Adoptees were given a narrative about their life story from their family, society, and the media from the time they joined their adoptive family. They must find their own voice. The strongest voice that speaks to them is what they have stored in their thoughts and emotions over time. This journal offers an adoptee the opportunity to carefully examine their perspectives and feelings about their life and to clarify what is truth and what serves them in their life journey. With clarity can spring emotional well-being. This journal is long overdue, and I love that the insightful questions are posed over a year's time so that a person can think, digest, and integrate any new revelations."

—**Sharon Kaplan Roszia**, co-author of *Seven Core Issues in Adoption and Permanency: A Comprehensive Guide to Promoting Understanding and Healing in Adoption, Foster Care, Kinship Families and Third-Party Reproduction*

"*Voices Unheard: A Reflective Journal for Adult Adoptees* is an important guide for adopted persons. The workbook is just right for digging deeper into the emotional landscape we need to explore in this lifetime journey of healing and discovery."

—**Deborah Jiang-Stein**, adoptee, author of *Prison Baby: A Memoir*, Founder, unPrison Project

" *Voices Unheard: A Reflective Journal for Adult Adoptees* is everything adoptees may not have realized they needed—a map for understanding their earliest traumatic experiences and navigating their adoption journeys. With a prompt for every week of the year based on core themes that arise in therapy, it facilitates reflective journaling—a strategy that can help adoptees gain insight, explore, and validate their feelings, comfort themselves, and, ultimately, reclaim their narratives. It's a vital tool as well for therapists who want to better understand the emotional lives of adoptees and an indispensable guide to help peer group leaders facilitate healing conversation. I highly recommend it."

—**B.K. Jackson**, editor of *Severance Magazine*

"Sharing my story about life as an orphan has revealed one thing more than any other: stories of the orphan and the adopted stay with us for our entire lives. What *Voices Unheard: A Reflective Journal for Adult Adoptees* does is allow us to take control of that narrative, to put our own experiences into our own words, and in doing so find measures of grace, understanding and healing."

—**Steve Pemberton**, author of *A Chance in the World: An Orphan Boy, a Mysterious Past, and How He Found a Place Called Home*

"*Voices Unheard: A Reflective Journal for Adult Adoptees* bravely breaks through the mystery of the unspoken. This guide offers a map for adoptees, one that urges us to listen to the truth of our bodies—the only kind of map we can trust. With nuts-and-bolts information such as terminology and scripts for running peer meetings, Lisa Coppola lays a path for those seeking the authentic voice and elusive truth—not just another story. With writing exercises that leave space for imagining and dreaming, the journal opens the gate to the layered, complicated trauma of the closed room, the bolted door of the adoptee's psyche."

—**Jan Beatty**, adoptee, author of **American Bastard**

"This is more than a workbook, it's a mirror and an amplifier for adoptees to reassert our autonomy and rewrite the narratives that are all too often made without us."

—**Nate Bae Kupel,** adoptee, President Emeritus, **Boston Korean Adoptees, Inc.**

"Adoptees coming out of the fog have much in common with people in recovery, and writing is a valuable tool not only because it aids in emotional healing, but because adoptees have important stories that need to be told. That Lisa Coppola, an adoption therapist and adoptee herself, wrote *Voices Unheard: A Reflective Journal for Adult Adoptees* in the format of a twelve-step meeting script adds helpful measures to protect the emotions of potentially vulnerable participants as they respond to the prompts and prepare to share what they've written.

"There are as many paths as there are adoptees; this journal allows for all adoptees to come together in a room and heal. Whether they are international or domestic adoptees, transracial or not, in reunion, just obtaining their official birth certificate, or they grew up in an open adoption—wherever the adoptee is in their process, the format gives guidelines preventing advice giving and crosstalk, and offers timed shares in round-robin format so everyone who wants to share has the opportunity to do so in a relatively safe space.

"This journal, replete with adoption-related glossary and bibliography, is everything the therapist leading an adoptee or group of adoptees, peer adoptee-group moderator, and adult adoptee working individually needs. With 52 writing prompts that center around the seven core issues that those in the adoption triad face—loss, rejection, guilt and shame, grief, identity, intimacy, and mastery/control—and space to write directly in the journal, at one meeting a week, the journal could take a year. Alternatively, a self-paced individual or group could work through it faster or use it any other way.

"I love this journal already. I teach creative writing classes, and the one I love teaching the most is Writing Personhood: For Adoptees. I plan to use these prompts in my classes! Thank you, BPAR and Lisa, for writing it for us all."

—**Aimee Christian**, adoptee, Voices Unheard: Real Adoptee Stories forum speaker, freelance writer published in **The New York Times, The Washington Post**

Voices Unheard
A Reflective Journal for Adult Adoptees

Lisa Coppola, LMHC

Hey Beth,
I'd take a Bullet
for you.
LC

Boston Post Adoption Resources

BPÅR
Boston Post Adoption Resources

Cover artwork by Kelly and Albie DiBenedetto
Editing by Lucy Davis
Design by Ilene Bezahler

ISBN 978-0-578-36683-8 (paperback)
ISBN 979-8-218-03161-9 (ebook)

This book is for all of you out there searching for your story and for Jennifer Eckert who supports so many of us in finding ours, and who was brave enough to find her own.

CONTENTS

The moon for many adopted or relinquished people represents the mystery of our lives, of our biological families and backgrounds. As children we may have looked up to the moon and wondered if our biological parents were also looking at that same moment. It may have been the only way we could imagine an ongoing connection to them. The fog represents the concept of denial most adult adoptees have experienced to some extent about the profound and complex impacts of our adoption. The ladder represents moving toward exploration of these impacts and away from the denial in order to lead more authentic and fulfilling lives.

A Special Letter to Adoptees

Welcome Adoptees,

I am so glad you found your way to this journal. I created it for you with love to aid you with exploring your truths.

  A little about how I got here. I grew up in a home of adoptees. We all arrived at the Coppola household through the Department of Children and Family Services, none of us biologically related to each other. Each of the three of us came from some kind of difficult circumstance, as is always the case with those relinquished or taken from their biological parents. Our parents, doing the best they could, tried in many ways to love us enough to heal us. They even formed the New Hampshire Open Door Society, a support group for adoptive parents, in 1980. Despite their vigorous pursuit of information which they sought from various psychologists, doctors, and therapists around the adoptee experience, they, like most if not all adoptive parents, struggled to truly accept and validate the impact of the various traumas each of us carried with us when we arrived. Along with their ignorances, they also did many things right. I remember often being around other adoptees as a young kid.

  "The Group," as our family very affectionately called it, got together often. We would go apple picking and camping in the White Mountains, and we celebrated the holidays together. Because of The Group, we were able to be introduced to the notion that we belonged, that we fit in somewhere. Our childhood friends in The Group didn't look like their parents, and neither did we. On some level, we kids may have thought that being adopted was even typical. Our bodies, hearts, and impulses, however, disagreed. Those parts of us knew innately that the separation from our biological parents and our genetic and cultural background was not typical. We reacted on a regular basis in varied ways to both the emotional and physiological traumas of our losses. Many of us were diagnosed with attention deficit disorders, reactive attachment disorders, obsessive compulsive disorders, and depression, without having any idea that the underlying problem did not originate from who we were, but rather resulted from what happened to us.

  When I was in my thirties, I joined an "Adult Adoptee" group in Boston. We met in a café and spilled our stories to each other. I remember shaking from the adrenaline of being with the others and trying to lift my coffee to my mouth without spilling it all over myself. Some of the group, in their adult lives, had met their birth parents and learned more about their identities and life before adoption. Some of them had pieced together a more complex narrative about how their early trauma impacted their lives. Some had been rejected by their biological families or their adoptive families. Some had experienced racism that had gone unacknowledged their entire lives by their white parents. All of them had wondered about where they came from. All of them had suffered a kind of grief throughout their lives that they couldn't quite understand. I instantly felt overcome with connection and experienced a kind of empathic love for each person in this group as I listened to their stories. Nothing had ever grounded me as well as hearing someone saying, "Me, too. I have been there."

"Nothing had ever grounded me as well as hearing someone saying, 'Me, too. I have been there.'"

In the 1990s there was a jump in research around adoptee mental health, but much of the research involved gathering information from school settings and adoptive parents. Adoptee voices have been vastly overlooked in adoption research, yet this perspective is essential for our healing as well as for helping adoptive parents, birth parents, the psychiatric system, and our society in general to understand our challenges.

Now as a seasoned Licensed Mental Health Counselor, in my specific work with adult adoptees, I constantly encounter deep feelings of inner turmoil, grief, disconnection, and, at times, overwhelming fear and anxiety stemming from those old, unattended wounds. Along with the confusion and difficulty of navigating biological reunion, exploring the adoptee experience can feel isolating to the adoptees who may not know others who can relate to it. I have dedicated much of my career to helping adoptees write about their stories and their changing realities. My workshops and open mic events called "Voices Unheard: Real Adoptee Stories" allow them to connect with each other during the creative process and heal together as a group.

Unfortunately, it is common for the actuality of childhood relinquishment to be minimized or unheard by others who are not adopted. When the fuller, more complicated truth of an adoptee's story is suppressed, it contributes further to what we adoption professionals call adoption loss trauma. Being adopted is complicated. It can be both a win and a loss at the same time, and when the "loss" part goes unacknowledged, the omission adds greatly to the complication. We know that being adopted is much more nuanced than simply, "Your mother wanted to give you a better life and then we got you. . . . The end." That widely accepted narrative often told to the adoptee encourages the harmful suppression of the multi-layered story that often holds loss, identity, shame, mystery, trauma, fear, loyalty, resiliency, and love.

"Being adopted is complicated. It can be both a win and a loss at the same time."

The prompts that I have created for you in this journal were motivated by taking a thorough inventory of the most prevalent difficult adult adoptee experiences reported by Boston Post Adoption Resources' clinicians such as: a considerable fear of loss or abandonment which impacts intimate relationships; trouble with personal boundaries; confusion around identity; and, almost always, issues around control and addictive behaviors.

As a psychotherapist specializing in dual diagnosis, I have worked for over a decade with people struggling with addictions such as substance abuse disorder and other behavioral compulsions. A substantial number of my clients have been adopted people. In my experience, I have seen that my adopted clients often start to experience an influx of attachment-related anxiety as they attempt to navigate their sobriety. I have taken many of those ideas and applied them to the prompts in the journal portion of this book. For readers who want to experience the prompts in a group setting, I provide detailed group leadership guidance for moderators based on a lifetime of experience in and running peer-run support groups.

The themes in my prompts align with the work of Silverstein and Kaplan from their 1982 article "The Core Experiences in Adoption," in which they found themes of loss, rejection, shame and guilt, grief, identity, intimacy, mastery and control throughout their work with adopted people (Silverstein and Kaplan, 1982).

Sometimes people can recognize reasons for their pain through visual memory, but for adoptees and those with early childhood trauma, the source might not be so clear. Dr. Julie Lopez, an adoptee herself, describes our implicit memory and how it works in greater detail in her 2019 book, *Live Empowered, Rewire Your Brain's Implicit Memory to Thrive in Business, Love and Life*. We learn that memories may be manifested through our reactions such as fear, anxiety, or aversion. These memories are not visual or explicit; instead, they are implicit and embedded within the systems of the body. According to the National Scientific Council on the Developing Child (2004), "Stated simply, as young children develop, their early emotional experiences literally become embedded in the architecture of their brains" (p. 1). Many of us cope with those painful early experiences that have stayed with us by using a variety of subconscious behaviors such as avoidance of or addiction to love relationships; perfectionism and people pleasing; substance abuse; and cutting. Dr. Gabor Maté (2012) concludes, "Abandonment, neglect, or abuse (emotional, physical or sexual) can alter physical stress mechanisms and the child often becomes more reactive to stress throughout their life. Substance abuse or dependence is related to stress response in an attempt to self-soothe" (p. 61). Addictive behavior of any kind can be a self-protective attempt to numb that implicit memory pain. The problem with numbing this pain, though, is that we then keep it lodged within ourselves, and it prevents us from experiencing the fuller growth we need in order to become our more authentic selves. So many of us are suffering with addiction. It is not surprising that research indicates that the prevalence of any lifetime substance use disorder is higher among adoptees when compared to non-adoptees (Yoon et al., 2012).

My hope is that, when you write about these issues in this weekly journal and then explore them further with an adoption trauma-informed professional, peer group, or other trusted support, your feelings may rise to the surface, where you can recognize, validate, and learn to comfort them.

Lisa Coppola, adoptee, LMHC, MEd

"This process will allow you to make room for a deeper healing experience that will promote authenticity, a more secure sense of identity, and in turn, a more rewarding life."

Introduction

All adult adoptees undoubtedly, at some point, become curious about their early lives when they were separated from their biological family and how that key part of their personal history has consciously or subconsciously affected their instincts, behaviors, and emotions. *Voices Unheard: A Reflective Journal for Adult Adoptees* provides an opportunity to process these experiences in a unique way on one's own, with a therapist, or through leading a peer support group. Through the act of reflective journaling, adoptees can build a better understanding of their own stories of being uprooted and replanted into an often (but not always) non-biological family. The creative process can enable the writer to recognize, validate, and learn how to comfort feelings, an essential step on the path to leading a healthy and productive life.

This journal contains 52 writing prompts to enable adoptees to explore their experiences. The prompts are built around themes that clinicians typically encounter in therapy with adoptees: loss, identity, control, intimacy, boundaries, information gathering and reunion, resilience, and healing.

I have also included an outline to guide adoptees who want to start and run peer-led adoptee support groups incorporating this journal.

A post-adoption vocabulary section and a list of suggested reading material provide an enhanced understanding of the concepts underlying the development of this journal, which was created with the support of a seasoned team of adoption-competent therapists at Boston Post Adoption Resources.

Who Can Benefit from this Journal

Voices Unheard: A Reflective Journal for Adult Adoptees can be used in three distinct ways:

- Adult adoptees can use the journal as a guide individually or under the care of a therapist.

- Therapists can use the journal as a tool in their practice with adopted clients.

- Peer-led support group moderators can use the prompts as weekly assignments to prepare adoptees in advance and enable attendees to benefit from the value of sharing their thoughts and opening a dialogue in a group setting. The journal offers guidelines and a script to help volunteer moderators run their group.

Please note that an intentional decision was made to focus specifically on adoptees for this journal. We recognize the trauma and challenges experienced by individuals who grew up in the foster care system and respect and appreciate that their challenges can differ from those of individuals who were adopted. Growing up and aging out of foster care or living in out-of-home placements are very unique and different experiences, and we felt that separating them out and focusing solely on the adoptee in this book is the best way to honor and respect these differences.

A Note to Adult Adoptees Using this Journal

As an adult adoptee navigating complicated life experiences, considering or venturing into reunion, and stepping out of the fog into new realizations around your adoption experience, you will gain insight from use of the exploratory prompts in this journal. The journal can be used in conjunction with therapy, as part of an adoptee peer-run or facilitator-run support group, or on one's own.

Please note that sometimes, doing the work of a prompted journal can bring up a lot of emotions, a normal part of healing. Take this work at your own pace. If emotions start to feel overwhelming when you use this journal, you might want to take a break. Utilize support such as your therapist, peers, and groups. Trauma-informed mental health clinicians trained in adoption competency, such as the team at Boston Post Adoption Resources, can provide the most appropriate support.

A Note to Therapists Using this Journal

For clinicians seeing adult adoptee clients, this 52-week journal works well as a tool while providing weekly therapy or group therapy. It can also be used as a guide for support groups in order to address and explore common adoptee experiences and themes by sharing responses to the weekly prompts over the course of a year.

This resource can help fill a gap in our educational system. While attachment theory and early childhood trauma was discussed in our graduate-school psychology classes, adoption loss trauma was barely touched upon, if discussed at all. In fact, the typical psychology graduate student spends 7.95 minutes learning about adoption (Dennis, 2014, p. 28). I believe that good treatment for adoptees should build relational trust through a focus on appropriate therapist transparency and allow a space for the adoptee's inner pain to be recognized, maybe for the first time, in a safe way. Exposure to peer-based social settings, trauma- and grief-informed therapy, as well as an ongoing longer-term therapeutic relationship are key components of adoption trauma-informed therapy.

Recommended Reading for Therapists Working with Adult Adoptees

Seven Core Issues in Adoption and Permanency; A Comprehensive Guide to Promoting Understanding and Healing in Adoption, Foster Care Kinship Families and Third Party Reproduction by Sharon Kaplan Roszia and Allison Davis Maxon

Adoption Therapy: Perspectives from Clients and Clinicians on Processing and Healing Post-Adoption Issues by Laura Dennis and Marcy Axness

A Note to Adult Adoptee Peer-Led Support Group Moderators Using this Journal

Adoptee-to-adoptee connection is irreplaceable. Just as two people in recovery from addiction benefit from the magic of group settings, adoptees can start to heal and feel understood when they have an opportunity to talk about their shared issues. Peer-led support groups, sometimes referred to as self-help support groups, enable this kind of connection in a setting where group members meet to provide mutual support without the assistance of professional moderators.

For the organizer, both the creation and moderation of an adult adoptee peer-led group can be a rewarding experience. The job of moderator works best on a volunteer basis. No single person should be in control of the group; the experience of a peer group works best as a democratic, shared experience. We follow the time-tested example of Alcoholics Anonymous, where the meetings are always peer led on a volunteer basis. This sense of mutuality throughout the process is an essential part of recovery. Research provides compelling evidence that recovering alcoholics who help other alcoholics are better able to maintain their own sobriety (Pagano, et. al., 2004, p. 770).

Adult Adoptee Peer Support Groups Using the Voices Unheard Journal

Peer support offers a level of understanding, authentic empathy, and validation often not available in professional relationships (Mead and McNeil, 2004 p. 4). Peer-to-peer connections are quite special and irreplaceable. This journal can be an excellent tool for moderating peer-led adult adoptee support groups. The theme-based prompts provide structure to the sessions so all participants can prepare in advance and focus on a specific topic.

When planning a support group for adult adoptees, it could be most beneficial to utilize group guidelines and some form of the script below.

Suggested Guidelines

- Meetings should last 1 hour to 1.5 hours, depending on the group size.

- Assign a designated moderator for each meeting. The moderator's job is to:

  1. Welcome people and share the locations of facilities such as bathrooms, water, exits, etc.

  2. Read Group Guidelines and Script.

Steps for Starting an Adult Adoptee Peer Support Group

- Start building your group by contacting anywhere from two to eight adoptees and inviting them. You might use language like the following:

> *Hey, I'm organizing an adult adoptee peer support group. This is a group for adult adoptees who are interested in exploring our experiences together through guided journaling prompts, which are done prior to the meeting. The meeting time is intended to share responses to the prompt and support one another. We would encourage regular attendance, but we wouldn't require it. Would you be interested in helping me start this kind of group?*

If they say yes, ask them to think of two other adoptees to invite as well.

- You can decide together on a venue, whether it's someone's home, a rented room in a library, or a church basement, a coffee shop, or an online space. Choose somewhere that will be reliable.

- Also decide if you want the group to meet weekly, biweekly, or monthly. (While this journal offers 52 writing prompts, enough to cover a full year of weekly meetings, the work can be done more quickly or spread out over years.)

- Then after the venue is chosen along with the first group date, the group might choose additional ways to reach out to other adoptees and encourage them to join.

- Contact everyone with the date and weekly venue.

- Decide who will take the role of the moderator of the first meeting, or volunteer yourself for that role.

Group Guidelines and Script for the Support Group Moderator

1. The volunteer moderator may use the following welcome script at meetings.

Welcome to the (insert your group name) Peer Support Group. This is a place for adoptees to explore our stories and connect with each other as a process in our healing. Weekly attendance, while encouraged, is not required to belong to the group.

We encourage folks to bring their Voices Unheard journals with them each time and come prepared after already exploring the week's assigned prompt in writing. Please note that sometimes, doing the work of a prompted journal or attending a group can bring up a lot of emotions, a normal part of healing. Take this work at your own pace. If emotions start to feel overwhelming, you might want to take a break or seek support from a trusted family member, a friend, or a professional.

If this is your first meeting, you can simply share your thoughts on the prompt for the week.

You can choose to read just a section from your Voices Unheard journal or all of what you wrote. You can also simply talk about what you wrote. Please keep in mind there will be a time limit, and if you have written a lot, consider which sections of writing you may want to share the most.

People who haven't written on the prompt over the week will still be invited to share their thoughts and feelings if they want.

Sharing will take place in a round-robin style and is always optional, meaning you may pass when it's your turn.

Please keep in mind that everyone is at a different point along their own journeys. Knowing this is of utmost importance to allow all experiences to be heard. After a person shares, as a general rule, there will be no responding or what is referred to as "verbal crosstalk," a rule practiced in 12-step meetings to promote a more active listening style within the group. Though this policy may seem awkward at first, it is meant to ensure that every person's experience is heard respectfully without advice, suggestions, or coercion into a different way of being or thinking. If they wish, people can talk more openly to each other about what they shared after the meeting has ended.

We will now set a time limit on sharing and give a one-minute warning before the time is up. This ensures that everyone who wants to share will have a turn. The warning signal will be a wave of the hand from the timekeeper. Of course, no one is required to share for the full length of their allotted time, and it is possible we will end early. Can I get a volunteer timekeeper?

2. At the conclusion of the welcome script, calculate the time limit per person based on the remainder of time and the number of people at the meeting. For example, if there are seven members and 50 minutes left, then each person can share for seven minutes, and the timekeeper will wave a one-minute warning at six minutes.

3. Now read the writing prompt chosen to be shared at this meeting.

4. After reading the prompt, ask who would like to share first. Explain to the group that after the first person shares, the option to share will move to the next person counter-clockwise, in a round-robin fashion, until everyone has had a turn to share or pass. Then, begin the sharing process.

5. At the end of the meeting, ask for a new volunteer to moderate the next meeting.

6. Read aloud the writing prompt for the next meeting and remind everyone to come prepared by writing in advance.

7. Thank everyone for coming, then end the meeting.

Post Adoption Vocabulary

Relevant words and definitions as they are recognized in this journal

ADOPTION- AND TRAUMA-INFORMED THERAPIST: a clinician who is well-versed on and practices attachment and trauma-informed interventions in order to address core adoption issues.

ADOPTION LOSS:

– the loss of the bond between birth family and adoptee, or the loss of biological connection

– the loss of what life may have been like without the cultural, psychological and emotional disruption of early separation

– the loss of genetic, racial, and ancestral background

– the loss of the story and witness to an adoptee's birth and first days or years

– the loss of trust as a first experience if one was separated from their mother early in life

– for the late discovery adoptee (LDA), a loss of trust in reality

ADVERSE CHILDHOOD EXPERIENCES (ACEs): CDC-Kaiser Permanente Adverse Childhood Experiences (ACE) Study is one of the largest investigations of childhood abuse and neglect and household challenges and later-life health and well-being. The original ACE Study was conducted at Kaiser Permanente from 1995 to 1997. The study found that toxic stress from potentially traumatic events in childhood (age 0-17) can change brain development and affect how the body responds to stress. High ACE scores are linked to multiple risk factors for several of the leading causes of death in adults (Felitti et al., 1998).

ATTACHMENT: the process by which an infant forms an emotional bond. Early attachment theorists include John Bowlby, Mary Ainsworth, Mary Main, and Harry Harlow. We know that when early attachment is disrupted, this can cause what mental health professionals refer to as an *insecure attachment style* that can travel with a person into adulthood. Having an insecure attachment style manifests differently in each person's behavior in relationships. For example, while one adult might avoid emotional intimacy, another might become clingy and dependent. Recent research has shown that attachment styles can change and become more secure with age and with experience in relationships (Chopik et al., 2019).

CORE ISSUES IN ADOPTION: Silverstein & Kaplan (1982) suggest that adoption triggers the seven following lifelong or core issues for all triad members, adoptees, birth parents and adoptive parents, regardless of the circumstances of the adoption or the characteristics of the participants:

1. loss
2. rejection
3. guilt and shame
4. grief
5. identity
6. intimacy
7. mastery/control

FIVE PROTECTIVE FACTORS: For someone who has early complex trauma, as experienced by all adoptees, protective factors may be seen as positive, countering events to improve outcomes and promote well-being. According to the Strengthening Families Approach and Protective Factors Framework (2014), "The five Strengthening Families protective factors are parental resilience, social connections, knowledge of parenting and child development, social and emotional competence of children, and concrete support in times of need" (Harper Browne, 2014, p. 21).

GENEALOGICAL BEWILDERMENT: a term initially coined by psychologist H. J. Sants in 1964. This concept was further introduced in 1952 to the *Journal of Mental Health* by psychiatrist E. Wellisch in a letter titled, "Children without Genealogy, a Problem of Adoption." Wellisch describes the potential identity problems that might be experienced by a child who has not met or is lacking in information about their biological parents.

HEALING: While healing is an individualized experience, it could be thought of as an authentic integration of one's suffering and life difficulties into new experiences of meaning and purpose. One 2005 study that looked at how people define healing found that "healing is an intensely personal, subjective experience involving a reconciliation of the meaning an individual ascribes to distressing events with his or her perception of wholeness as a person" (Egnew, 2005, p. 255).

HYPERAROUSAL: Essentially, when reminded of a trauma, the body goes into a state of high alert to prepare to handle a threat of danger, even when there is actually no real danger at hand. When we consider the trauma of abandonment, when the baby loses the sound, scent, and all the physiological regulation it receives from its birth mother, we may consider how a resulting hyperarousal may later play out in the body when the child, and also the eventual adult, perceives and then prepares for another abandonment. The Substance Abuse and Mental Health Services Administration (2014) explains hyperarousal, also called hypervigilance, as "the body's way of remaining prepared" (p. 65).

IMPLICIT MEMORIES: memories embedded in our systems that we might not remember visually but that can have a profound effect on our feelings and behavior. This concept was developed in the early 1900s by a number of scientists in a variety of different disciplines including Douglass McDougall, who in 1923 wrote about explicit and implicit recognition. More recently, Dr. Julie Lopez (2019), who is also an adoptee, explores past experiences and their impact in her book, *Live Empowered! Rewiring Your Brain's Implicit Memory to Thrive in Business, Love and Life.* Regarding an experience of separation from a biological mother, therapists may also describe this notion as *body or pre-verbal memory.* Dr. Bruce Perry is a renowned expert in the field of early childhood trauma and its impact on the developing mind. According to Perry (2000), "The majority of our memories are non-cognitive and preverbal. It is the experiences of early childhood that create the foundational organization of neural systems that will be used for a lifetime" (p. 294).

INNER CHILD OR INNER CHILDREN: Through the lens of a parts mindset (see *parts mindset* below in Post Adoption Vocabulary), inner children are parts of us that are still in pain from infancy, toddlerhood, or any part of childhood. Examples might be an inner infant who is yearning for their mother to return; an inner toddler who feels impulsive and restless or ashamed; or an inner teenager who feels something is just wrong about who they are or how they show up in the world. Psychologist Carl Jung is considered to have coined the term *inner children.* The concept of inner children or inner child is applied to many different areas throughout psychology and self-help communities today. Inner child work often includes a person connecting with a visualization of their own inner child and providing that inner child the love, compassion, and nurturing now that they needed but may not have received in childhood.

INTIMACY: a bond of emotional connection in which the range of human experiences— the good, the bad, the ugly, and all the in-betweens—are shared and seen by all parties.

INTUITION: a deeper wisdom from within you that knows what you want and need.

KINSHIP ADOPTION: when the child, infant or teenager is legally placed with relatives or kin. Kinship adoption is sometimes called *relative adoption*.

LATE DISCOVERY ADOPTEE: sometimes referred to as an *LDA*, a person who learns in adulthood that they were adopted as a child.

NARRATIVE THERAPY: an empowering form of counseling that views people as separate from their problems and explores more deeply the stories people carry with them about who they are and how they draw meaning from their lives. Clients are considered to be the experts on their own lives. With this new perspective, individuals feel more empowered to make changes in their thought patterns and behavior and can "rewrite" their life stories for a future that reflects who they want to be, what they are capable of, and what their purpose is, separate from their problems.

ORIGINAL FAMILY OR FIRST FAMILY: how we, as adoptees, may choose to refer to our original biological mother and father; may also be called *birth family* or *natural family*.

OUT OF THE FOG: Many in the adoptee community use the term "out of the fog" to describe the experience of an adopted person who is in the midst of gaining deep insights, sometimes rapidly, into their past suppressed experiences.

PARTS MINDSET: If we have a parts mindset, we think about ourselves in terms of parts versus one whole being. This allows us to consider the needs and agenda of different sides (or parts) of us. For example: Some of these parts are wounded parts, some are protective parts, some parts are also different ages, some parts get triggered more than others, some parts accept love more than others. Adoptees could be said to have an inner child part or infant part that may need extra love and compassion throughout their lives. Sometimes we have protective parts that may be misguided, such as a part that uses shame to hush a nervous anxious part. *Parts work* is explored more extensively in counseling through theories such as internal family systems and inner child work.

PRIMAL WOUND: a term coined by Nancy Verrier to describe the wound that develops when a mother and child are separated after childbirth. She writes, "The resultant experience of abandonment and loss is indelibly imprinted upon the unconscious minds of these children, causing that which I call the Primal Wound" (Verrier, 1993, p.1).

PROVIDER ROLE: a pressure to perform in a certain way that an adoptee feels either intuitively out of loyalty to parents or due to implied or explicitly stated expectations expressed by others.

RELINQUISHMENT: when a birth parent gives up his or her parental rights. This may or may not be done voluntarily.

RELINQUISHEE: a person who was relinquished from their biological parents.

RESILIENCE: one's ability to adapt to and engage in growth from difficult life situations.

SECONDARY REJECTION: experiencing another rejection by family after the initial relinquishment, following an attempt at communication or a reunion. This experience of non-acceptance, non-approval, or non-support triggers the original wound of abandonment rejection.

SHAME: social science researcher Dr. Brené Brown (2013) defines shame as, "the intensely painful feeling or experience of believing that . . . something we've experienced, done, or failed to do makes us unworthy of connection."

THIRD-PERSON STORY STYLE: when the writer relates all the action of the story they are telling about themselves through externalization using only third-person pronouns such as "he," "she," and "they" to describe their own experiences.

TRANSRACIAL ADOPTION: when a child who is of one race or ethnic group is placed with adoptive parents of another race or ethnic group.

Suggested Reading

Nonfiction Books About Adoption

20 Life-Transforming Choices Adoptees Need to Make, Second Edition by Sherrie Eldridge (2015)

Adoption Is a Lifelong Journey by Kelly DiBenedetto, Katie Gorczyca, and Jennifer Eckert (2017)

The Adoption Reunion Survival Guide: Preparing Yourself for the Search, Reunion, and Beyond by Julie Jarrell Bailey and Lynn N. Giddens (2001)

Adoption Therapy: Perspectives from Clients and Clinicians on Processing and Healing Post-Adoption Issues edited by Laura Dennis (2014)

Being Adopted: The Lifelong Search for Self by David M. Brodzinsky, PhD, Marshall D. Schechter, MD, and Robin Marantz Henig (1993)

Coming Home to Self: The Adopted Child Grows Up by Nancy Newton Verrier (2003)

Journey of the Adopted Self: A Quest for Wholeness by Betty Jean Lifton (1995)

The Primal Wound: Understanding the Adopted Child by Nancy Newton Verrier (1993)

Seven Core Issues in Adoption and Permanency: A Comprehensive Guide to Promoting Understanding and Healing in Adoption, Foster Care Kinship Families and Third Party Reproduction by Sharon Roszia and Allison Davis Maxon (2019)

Twenty Things Adopted Kids Wish Their Adoptive Parents Knew by Sherrie Eldridge (1999)

Voices in Transracial Adoption: Insights from Adoptees, Parents, and Professionals by Boston Post Adoption Resources (2021)

What White Parents Should Know About Transracial Adoption: An Adoptee's Perspective on Its History, Nuances, and Practices by Melissa Guida-Richards (2021)

Memoirs About Adoption

After the Morning Calm: Reflections of Korean Adoptees edited by Dr. Sook Wilkinson and Nancy Fox (2002)

All You Can Ever Know: A Memoir by Nicole Chung (2018)

American Bastard: A Memoir by Jan Beatty (2021)

Before We Were Yours: A Novel by Lisa Wingate (2017)

A Chance in the World: An Orphan Boy, A Mysterious Past, and How He Found a Place Called Home by Steve Pemberton (2012)

Dear Stephen Michael's Mother: A Memoir by Kevin Barhydt (2020)

The Guild of the Infant Saviour: An Adopted Child's Memory Book by Megan Culhane Galbraith (2021)

Inconvenient Daughter: A Novel by Lauren J. Sharkey (2020)

In Their Own Voices: Transracial Adoptees Tell Their Stories by Rita J. Simon and Rhonda M. Roorda (2000)

Lost Daughters: Writing Adoption from a Place of Empowerment and Peace edited by Amanda H. L. Transue-Woolston, Julie Stromberg, Karen Pickell, and Jennifer Anastasi (2014)

Prison Baby: A Memoir by Deborah Jiang-Stein (2014)

Searching for Mom: A Memoir by Linda Easterly and Sara Easterly (2019)

Surviving the White Gaze: A Memoir by Rebecca Carroll (2021)

You Don't Look Adopted by Anne Heffron (2016)

Week 1

Theme: **IDENTITY**

Prompt: **CULTURAL PRESSURE**

Have you heard any of the following statements in response to your being adopted?

You're lucky, I wish I was adopted.

You were chosen.

I always thought I was adopted, too.

How did you feel when you heard this or a version of these statements? How have you responded over the years? In what ways might you have internalized these messages?

If you have not heard these or similar statements, how do you imagine your friends and adoptive family have perceived your experience of adoption? And how does this differ from how you might perceive your own experience?

Week 2

Theme: **INFORMATION GATHERING & REUNION**
Prompt: **QUESTIONS**

If you could have accurate answers to any ten questions about your biological history or life prior to relinquishment, what questions would you ask? Of those ten questions, which are your top three, and why?

How does it feel to know that you may never know many of the answers?

If some of these questions have already been answered, what has this process been like for you?

2

Theme: INFORMATION GATHERING & REUNION Prompt: QUESTIONS

Week 3
Theme: **INTIMACY**
Prompt: **SHAME . . . INTIMACY'S GREAT DISTANCER**

In what ways do you feel you might be inadequate?

Do you ever feel like an imposter? Describe this feeling and an example of how you may have coped with or resolved it in the past.

Where might adoption or transracial adoption play a role in these shame feelings?

How might shame be disconnecting you from intimacy?

If you experienced less shame, how might things be different for you?

3

Theme: **INTIMACY**   Prompt: **SHAME . . . INTIMACY'S GREAT DISTANCER**

Week 4

Theme: **HEALING**

Prompt: **CONNECTION**

Are you connecting with other adoptees for the first time in your life as an adult? If so, do you think it may have been different to have had this experience as a youth? How so?

If, on the other hand, you did know other adoptees as a youth, did it feel different to connect with peers when you were younger versus as an adult?

Write a short true story of connection between adoptees that feels impactful to you. If you can't think of an example, can you name a particular time in your life that you would have benefitted from connecting with another adoptee?

4

Theme: **HEALING** Prompt: **CONNECTION**

Week 5
Theme: **CONTROL**
Prompt: **LEARNING TRUST**

Think of a time you let go of control and trusted that you would be cared for—by other people, some higher power, the universe, nature, karma, or by what you might consider as god—by anything outside of yourself. Write about this time, even if it was a small moment in your life, and include any thoughts on how you allowed yourself that experience of trust.

5 Theme: **CONTROL** Prompt: **LEARNING TRUST**

Week 6
Theme: **LOSS**
Prompt: **OUT OF THE FOG**

The term *coming out of the fog* describes a person's journey of coming out of a very protective denial and gaining deep insights, sometimes rapidly, into their past experiences. Coming out of the fog will also bring grief. Grief will show up when you are no longer in denial of something that is painful.

Describe how your adoption grief is showing up today and how it has shown up in the past.

Where do you think you are in the fog? Deep in? Being pushed out? Is it behind you, yet still hovering nearby? Do you not believe in the fog?

Week 7

Theme: **BOUNDARIES**
Prompt: **HIGH & LOW BOUNDARIES**

Often adoptees struggle with having quite low or quite high boundaries. In both instances it may be that the person is trying to control the way others see them as a way to protect themselves. With low boundaries, if everyone knows their business, then no single individual can actually get closer than anyone else. With high boundaries, if nobody knows their business, then no one can actually get close at all.

What has your experience been like with noticing your boundary style or pattern? How might this pattern be protecting you? What might this pattern be taking from you? What part of you is this pattern coming from? Describe that *part* in age, personality, and motive.

7

Theme: **BOUNDARIES**   Prompt: **HIGH & LOW BOUNDARIES**

Week 8
Theme: **IDENTITY**
Prompt: **DISCONNECTION**

Write about a time where you felt like a stranger either to your own body or like a stranger in your own family. Try writing this in first-person or third-person story style describing a particular memory or set of memories.

Week 9

Theme: **INFORMATION GATHERING & REUNION**

Prompt: **FAMILY TREES**

What was your experience like in school when family tree, genetics, or ancestral history projects were discussed? Try writing out a scene in which you are a child back in school during this time. Maybe try writing this in third-person story style.

9

Theme: **INFORMATION GATHERING & REUNION** Prompt: **FAMILY TREES**

Week 10
Theme: **INTIMACY**
Prompt: **VISUALIZATION**

Describe in detail an example of an intimate partnership you admire. What do you admire? How do the partners deal with conflict? How do they connect with each other?

Do you believe something similar is possible for you? Why or why not?

If not, how might you need to change in order to be ready for this type of intimacy?

Theme: **INTIMACY** Prompt: **VISUALIZATION**

Week 11

Theme: **HEALING**

Prompt: **PROTECTIVE FACTORS**

Anyone who has been relinquished has experienced complex trauma and/or deep loss. The *Five Protective Factors* are positive, countering events that may help the person thrive in their life despite their Adverse Childhood Experiences (ACEs). The five factors are: parental resilience, social connections, concrete support in times of need, knowledge of parenting and child development, and social and emotional competence of children.

Which protective factors were present in your childhood?

Which protective factors were missing, and how did this gap play a role in your younger years?

Week 12

Theme: **CONTROL**

Prompt: **UNMANAGEABILITY**

Write about a situation in your past which you desperately attempted to control, but which, in retrospect, you can now see was actually out of your realm of control. What attempts did you make to control things? What attempts did you make to control your feelings around the situation? Did you realize at some point that things were becoming unmanageable for you?

Week 13
Theme: **LOSS**
Prompt: **TRUST**

Describe an experience in which you have lost trust in those close to you in a way which may not have appeared logical to others, or even to yourself. How might this experience have been rooted in your experience of adoption loss?

If you are a Late Discovery Adoptee who was first told as an adult about your relinquishment and adoption: How may this discovery have contributed to the loss of what you previously believed was the reality of your life? Describe your loss of trust in those closest to you.

Week 14

Theme: **BOUNDARIES**

Prompt: **HYPERAROUSAL**

As an adult in relationships, how have you reacted in moments when you have first perceived that trust may have been damaged or broken by another? How have you coped with the feelings that come along with this? Suggestion: Get specific in your writing. If possible, describe your coping strategies, no matter how "dysfunctional" they may seem, through several different examples.

How are these strategies working for you and protecting you? How might they also be working against you?

Theme: **BOUNDARIES**   Prompt: **HYPERAROUSAL**

Week 15

Theme: **IDENTITY**

Prompt: **PARTS MINDSET**

Thinking about ourselves in terms of different emotionally charged parts rather than one whole being allows us to consider the needs and agenda of different sides (or parts) of us. Let's get to know some parts of you.

Introduce us to some of the parts of you that are wounded, protective, and empowered. Tell us about when and how these parts may have gotten their start. Tell us about their agendas and how they may be trying to protect you. You might consider drawing them out as illustrations or diagrams—whatever feels right.

Week 16
Theme: **INFORMATION GATHERING & REUNION**
Prompt: **ENVY**

Have you experienced envy around another adoptee's reunion experiences? How about envy or other painful feelings around your friends' or other biological family members' familial relationships? What has this envy been like for you? How has it impacted your own journey?

How might you allow yourself to feel your feelings as you consider starting or continue to navigate reunion?

Theme: **INFORMATION GATHERING & REUNION**   Prompt: **ENVY**

Week 17
Theme: **INTIMACY**
Prompt: **TRUST**

Write about a specific time when you found comfort and peace through a relationship. This relationship can involve a parent, sibling, romantic partner, or a friend. Describe the scene and the experience.

How did trust play a role?

Was there something in particular about that person that allowed for comfort and peace?

17

Theme: **INTIMACY**   Prompt: **TRUST**

Week 18
Theme: **HEALING**
Prompt: **INNER PARENT WORK**

Find a photo of yourself as a child. For five minutes look at this photo and imagine you are actually the loving parent of the child in the photo. Now imagine that this child in the photo is struggling with feelings of rejection and shame and has come to you for support. What would you say to comfort that child?

How does your role as a parent to that child differ from how you might actually treat and talk to yourself?

18

Theme: **HEALING**   Prompt: **INNER PARENT WORK**

Week 19

Theme: **CONTROL**

Prompt: **CONTROLLING THE NARRATIVE**

Have you ever found yourself wanting to reject someone before they had a chance to reject you, or found yourself jumping to conclusions about being rejected? Have you acted on those assumptions, and if so, what was the result of your actions?

Write about an experience like this either in first-person journaling form or in third person as if someone else was telling your story. Include your thoughts on how you may have experienced rejection through an adoption trauma lens and how you may have been attempting to protect yourself.

19

Week 20
Theme: **LOSS**

Prompt: **SHAME**

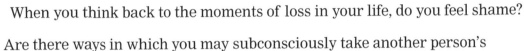

When you think back to the moments of loss in your life, do you feel shame?

Are there ways in which you may subconsciously take another person's inability (for instance their emotional unavailability or inability to empathize) personally, as though it's about who you are when in reality it's about them? What might this have to do with your early relinquishment and the theme of control?

20

Week 21
Theme: **BOUNDARIES**
Prompt: **PRESSURE**

How does pressure play a role in your life?

Do you feel a pressure to provide something for others so strongly at times that it either propels you into a fixing role or paralyzes you from making moves at all? Explore this.

How might fear play a role in this pressure?

How might you provide yourself some pressure relief?

21

Theme: **BOUNDARIES** Prompt: **PRESSURE**

Week 22

Theme: **IDENTITY**

Prompt: **NATURE & NURTURE**

What parts of your personality were most likely influenced by your adoptive parents? What parts seem to have come from within you and may possibly be hereditary? Explore any traits that you are especially curious about.

Considering white privilege, how was white privilege addressed or not addressed in your adoptive or biological family?

If you are transracially adopted, how was your race addressed or not addressed?

Week 23

Theme: **INFORMATION GATHERING & REUNION**

Prompt: **REQUESTING INFORMATION**

What was your experience like when you requested information about your own history from your adoptive parents or when you requested information from the agency that you were adopted through?

Describe your fears about requesting information if you haven't already done so. Write out the worst-case scenario, and then five other scenarios with different outcomes.

Theme: **INFORMATION GATHERING & REUNION** Prompt: **REQUESTING INFORMATION**

Week 24
Theme: **INTIMACY**
Prompt: **LOYALTY**

Many of us feel a strong loyalty to our adoptive families and struggle with talking to them about our adoption or reunion curiosities or experiences. In what ways might loyalty to your adoptive family be benefiting you? What might it be taking from you?

If you do not relate to this feeling of strong loyalty, what has it been like for you to communicate about these things with your adoptive family?

24

Theme: **INTIMACY** Prompt: **LOYALTY**

Week 25
Theme: HEALING
Prompt: BELONGING

Was there any character that you related to as a child who was also adopted or was raised by a non-biological family? Write a letter or poem to this character informing them of the impact they had on you.

And/or write a short story about a time in your childhood when you felt a sense of belonging. What aspects of the experience contributed to feeling like you belonged?

25

Theme: **HEALING** Prompt: **BELONGING**

Week 26
Theme: **CONTROL**

Prompt: **PRESSURE & PERFECTIONISM**

Has a part of you felt a pressure to be "perfect"? Write about a time that part of yourself felt this pressure.

What has it been like for that part of you, and what might the pressure to be perfect have to do with the theme of *control*?

How might your experience of being adopted play a role in this quest for perfectionism?

26

Theme: **CONTROL** Prompt: **PRESSURE & PERFECTIONISM**

Week 27
Theme: **LOSS**
Prompt: **ABANDONMENT**

Do you expect some form of abandonment from friends and loved ones? If so, how does this expectation protect you? What does this expectation take from you?

If you do not relate to this expectation of abandonment, what has it been like for you to trust in relationships?

Theme: **LOSS**   Prompt: **ABANDONMENT**

Week 28

Theme: **BOUNDARIES**

Prompt: **PROTECTING OURSELVES**

Do you struggle with implementing boundaries in order to protect yourself from other people's toxic energy or behavior? Describe this struggle and/or describe a time when you implemented strong boundaries to protect yourself.

Describe a time when you lowered your boundaries to allow for a deeper intimacy.

28

Theme: **BOUNDARIES** Prompt: **PROTECTING OURSELVES**

Week 29

Theme: **IDENTITY**

Prompt: **INFORMATION & IDENTITY**

How has reunion or new information about your genetic background contributed to your identity?

If you have not had experience with search or reunion and haven't found out new information, how has the lack of information contributed to your identity?

Theme: **IDENTITY** Prompt: **INFORMATION & IDENTITY**

Week 30

Theme: **INFORMATION GATHERING & REUNION**

Prompt: **BEING READY**

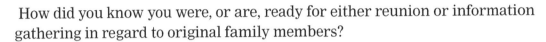

How did you know you were, or are, ready for either reunion or information gathering in regard to original family members?

What does or did your "being ready" feel like?

How might you know that you are "not ready"?

30

Theme: **INFORMATION GATHERING & REUNION**   Prompt: **BEING READY**

Week 31

Theme: **INTIMACY**

Prompt: **HEALTHY INTIMACY**

How would you describe healthy intimacy? How do you know when you are experiencing it?

When you experience intimacy, are there parts of yourself that feel hesitant or are reluctant to be intimate? If so, describe what these parts of yourself need and want.

Theme: **INTIMACY**   Prompt: **HEALTHY INTIMACY**

Week 32

Theme: **HEALING**

Prompt: **TELLING YOUR STORY**

Describe two experiences no matter how small each one might be:

1. the first time you were talking to another person about your adoption when you felt invalidated by the person you were talking to; and

2. a time where you felt heard, understood, and validated.

What was the difference between the two responses?

32

Theme: **HEALING**   Prompt: **TELLING YOUR STORY**

Week 33
Theme: **CONTROL**
Prompt: **SELF-COMPASSION**

Write a letter to your teenage self from your current self. Acknowledge how adoption or foster care experiences may have impacted your teenage self. Show compassion for your teenage self through the letter by acknowledging the things that were out of your control.

Week 34
Theme: **LOSS**
Prompt: **FEAR**

Loss has a profound effect on the body and mind. This can create a deep fear of potentially experiencing more loss in the future. In what situations do you experience this fear of additional losses? How does it impact your thoughts, feelings and behavior?

Theme: **LOSS** Prompt: **FEAR**

Week 35
Theme: **BOUNDARIES**
Prompt: **ATTACHMENT**

When our earliest attachment relationships are disrupted due to neglect, abuse, or relinquishment, this can create what professionals call an *insecure attachment style*. Instead of feeling secure in relationships, a person may tend to either avoid moments of intimacy or become anxious, controlling, or clingy when in relationships. If we are too focused on avoiding the pain of abandonment, then we might forget about what we even want and need. Only when we know what we really need can we sort out and communicate our boundaries in our relationships. Boundaries are how we can truly protect ourselves.

Do you know what your needs are in a relationship? List them and consider what your boundaries might be from this list.

Consider how things might be different if you were better able to more clearly communicate these needs and boundaries.

35

Theme: **BOUNDARIES** Prompt: **ATTACHMENT**

Week 36

Theme: **IDENTITY**

Prompt: **LACK OF ALIGNMENT**

An important part of identity development is to be able to see yourself mirrored in other people. It helps you make sense of who you are in the world and where you belong.

How do you make sense of your physical presence in the world considering the lack of biological family and/or the lack of racial alignment in your adoptive family?

Week 37

Theme: **INFORMATION GATHERING & REUNION**

Prompt: **REUNION FEARS & FANTASIES**

If you have not been in reunion, what fears do you have when you think about possible reunion with your birth family, and what fantasies do you have?

If you have been in reunion, what surprised you the most about your reunion experience? What advice might you give to someone embarking on a reunion journey?

Theme: **INFORMATION GATHERING & REUNION** Prompt: **REUNION FEARS & FANTASIES**

Week 38

Theme: **INTIMACY**

Prompt: **SHAME & REJECTION**

Do certain words or phrases around adoption bring up shame for you?

If you can think of an example in your life when you felt shame around your adoption, try to write about this in third-person story style with detail.

Week 39

Theme: **HEALING**
Prompt: **REPARENTING**

Sit down next to your inner child. If it is difficult to visualize this, you might want to find an object that represents your inner child, such as a photo, blanket, or stuffed animal. What do they need to hear from you today? How can you best protect and comfort them? Write out a dialogue between you and your inner child.

39

Theme: **HEALING** Prompt: **REPARENTING**

Week 40
Theme: **CONTROL**
Prompt: **COPING WITH UNCERTAINTY**

Write a story that illustrates how you have coped with times of uncertainty in the past, and then write a story about how you cope now. What has changed? How might things still need to change further?

When you think of your ideal mentor (this can be a real person or someone on a show or in a book), how might they cope with uncertainty?

Theme: **CONTROL** Prompt: **COPING WITH UNCERTAINTY**

Week 41

Theme: **LOSS**
Prompt: **DENIAL**

How has cultural or family denial of your adoption loss and/or of racism experienced as a transracial adoptee affected you? Write this as a short story. Think of a moment in which you felt confronted with this denial, and start your story there.

41

Theme: **LOSS** Prompt: **DENIAL**

Week 42
Theme: **BOUNDARIES**
Prompt: **RELATIONSHIPS**

Have you ever stayed in a relationship or friendship because you felt it would be good for the other person even though it wasn't beneficial for you?

Have you ever avoided a relationship because you felt too much pressure?

How might either of these experiences relate to adoption and the related pressure you might feel to take care of others?

Do you understand your needs in a relationship? If so, what has it been like for you to observe whether or not your needs are being met by your partner?

Week 43

Theme: **IDENTITY**
Prompt: **RESILIENCE**

When have you felt the most resilient in your adult life?

In what ways have you healed or saved yourself?

When have you felt like a survivor?

Week 44

Theme: **INFORMATION GATHERING & REUNION**

Prompt: **SECONDARY REJECTION**

Secondary rejection is experiencing another rejection by birth family after the initial relinquishment, following an attempt at communication or a reunion. This experience of non-acceptance, non-approval, or non-support triggers the original wound of abandonment rejection.

If you fear the possibility of secondary rejection, list your fears and how you worry they might impact you. Then visualize how you might move forward from a reunion rejection experience and describe this process as well.

If you have experienced secondary rejection, acknowledge this experience and the pain that has come with it. Write to your inner child and provide the love and support they need.

If reunion with your birth family has never been important to you, write about your decision to not search. Have your feelings about searching changed over the years?

44

Theme: **INFORMATION GATHERING & REUNION**   Prompt: **SECONDARY REJECTION**

Week 45

Theme: **INTIMACY**

Prompt: **SHAME & INTERGENERATIONAL TRAUMA**

When in your life might you have felt a "shame that is not yours to feel," or in other words, a sense of shame that has been passed down intergenerationally through your biological or adoptive family or directly through your adoptive family?

How is this shame manifesting in your relationships and affecting your experience of intimacy?

Week 46

Theme: **HEALING**

Prompt: **GROWTH**

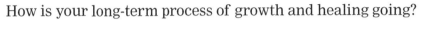

How is your long-term process of growth and healing going?

What areas do you need to give more attention to now? If you were able to move toward healing in those areas, how might things be different for you in your daily life?

Week 47
Theme: **CONTROL**
Prompt: **MENTORSHIP & POSITIVE CONTROL**

Consider some of the times in your life when you have felt the most resilient and strong. How were you able to find strength and courage during those times?

Who did you look to as an example of real strength and bravery?

47

Theme: **CONTROL** Prompt: **MENTORSHIP & POSITIVE CONTROL**

Week 48
Theme: **LOSS**
Prompt: **IMPLICIT MEMORIES**

Implicit memories are memories, sometimes preverbal from childhood, that we might not remember visually but may suddenly appear to come "out of nowhere" later in life. When they do surface through our behaviors or emotions, they can have a profound effect on us. For example, a 12-year-old adoptee might howl in despair when kittens are separated from the mother kitten, or an adult adoptee might feel a rush of immense grief at the sight of her best friend cuddling her newborn baby.

Write about a time when you had an experience with the rise of an implicit memory. Tip: This implicit memory trigger may have happened through a relationship of some sort, through watching a movie or show, or through witnessing an experience. It's a heavy wave of emotion that feels disproportionate to the current experience at hand.

Week 49

Theme: **BOUNDARIES**

Prompt: **HYPERAROUSAL**

How do you cope in the moment as an adult in a relationship when you perceive that trust has been damaged or broken through betrayal?

How do you cope once there has been some time and space from your immediate feelings?

Suggestion: Talk about two different examples.

Theme: **BOUNDARIES** Prompt: **HYPERAROUSAL**

Week 50

Theme: **IDENTITY**

Prompt: **BELONGING**

Is there a place or situation in your life such as a location, being around a group of people, or an activity where you feel the most at home and at ease? Describe this place and how you came upon it.

What role/s do you play in this place?

What has this place taught you about who you are?

Week 51
Theme: **INTIMACY**
Prompt: **VISUALIZING TRUST**

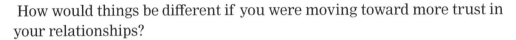

How would things be different if you were moving toward more trust in your relationships?

What do you need from another person to feel safe enough to move toward trust initially?

Week 52

Theme: **HEALING**

Prompt: **CONNECTION**

How did it feel to come out of the fog and start your healing journey with other adoptees on the same path?

What advice would you give an adoptee at the beginning of their journey of exploring their adoption more deeply?

Write out a personal story of healing connection that can only happen between adoptees.

References

Brown, B. (2013, January 15). Shame vs. guilt. BrenéBrown.com. https://brenebrown.com/articles/2013/01/15/shame-v-guilt/

Chopik, W. J., Edelstein, R. S., & Grimm, K. J. (2019). Longitudinal changes in attachment orientation over a 59-year period. *Journal of Personality and Social Psychology, 116*(4), 598–611. https://doi.org/10.1037/pspp0000167

Dennis, L. (2014). *Adoption therapy: Perspectives from clients and clinicians on processing and healing post-adoption issues.* Entourage Publishing.

Egnew, T. R. (2005). The meaning of healing: Transcending suffering. *The Annals of Family Medicine, 3*(3) 255–262. https://doi.org/10.1370/afm.313

Felitti, V. J., Anda, R. F., Nordenberg, D., Williamson, D. F., Spitz, A. M., Edwards, V., Koss, M. P., & Marks, J. S. (1998). Relationship of childhood abuse and household dysfunction to many of the leading causes of death in adults: The Adverse Childhood Experiences (ACE) Study. *American Journal of Preventive Medicine, 14*(4), 245–258. https://doi.org/10.1016/s0749-3797(98)00017-8

Harper Browne, C. (2014, September). The Strengthening Families approach and protective factors framework: Branching out and reaching deeper. Center for the Study of Social Policy. https://cssp.org/wp-content/uploads/2018/11/Branching-Out-and-Reaching-Deeper.pdf

Lopez, J. (2019). *Live empowered: Rewiring your brain's implicit memory to thrive in business, love, and life.* Lioncrest Publishing.

Maté, G. (2012). Addiction: Childhood trauma, stress and the biology of addiction. *Journal of Restorative Medicine, 1*(1), 56–63. https://journal.restorativemedicine.org/index.php/journal/article/view/12/19

McDougall, W. (1923). *Outline of psychology.* Charles Scribner's Sons.

Mead, S., & McNeil, C. (2006). Peer support: What makes it unique. *International Journal of Psychosocial Rehabilitation, 10*(2), 29–37.

National Scientific Council on the Developing Child. (2004). *Children's emotional development is built into the architecture of their brains: Working Paper No. 2.* https://46y5eh11fhgw3ve3ytpwxt9r-wpengine.netdna-ssl.com/wp-content/uploads/2004/04/Childrens-Emotional-Development-Is-Built-into-the-Architecture-of-Their-Brains.pdf

Pagano, M. E., Friend, K. B., Tonigan, J. S., & Stout, R. L. (2004). Helping other alcoholics in alcoholics anonymous and drinking outcomes: Findings from project MATCH. *Journal of Studies on Alcohol, 65*(6), 766–773.

Perry, B.D. (2000). Sexual abuse of infants. *Trauma, Violence & Abuse, 1*(3), 294-296. Sage Publications.

Silverstein, D., & Kaplan, S. (1982). *Lifelong issues in adoption.* https://www.americanadoptioncongress.org/grief_silverstein_article.php

Substance Abuse and Mental Health Services Administration. (2014). *Trauma-informed care in behavioral health services.* https://www.ncbi.nlm.nih.gov/books/NBK207201/pdf/Bookshelf_NBK207201.pdf

Verrier, N. (1993). *The primal wound: Understanding the adopted child.* Gateway Press.

Wellisch, E. (1952). Children without genealogy—A problem of adoption. *Journal of Mental Health,* 41-42. https://www.ncbi.nlm.nih.gov/pmc/articles/PMC5077842/

Yoon, G., Westermeyer, J., Warwick, M., & Kuskowski, M.A. (2012, November). Substance use disorders and adoption findings from a national sample. *PLOS ONE, 7*(11), 1–6. https://doi.org/10.1371/journal.pone.0049655

Acknowledgments

Thank you to the whole BPAR team for all of your help along the way. Thanks to Lucy Davis for your help editing and also for guiding me through this process. Thanks Maya Rogers-Bursen for being my co-host for the Voices Unheard forum. Thanks to Jennifer Eckert, Kelly DiBenedetto, Erica Kramer, Darci Nelson, KC Craig, and Marta Isabella Sierra for your extra eyes and help in the creation of this journal. Thank you to Kelly and Albie DiBenedetto for the beautiful cover illustration. Thank you to Ilene Bezahler for all the book design expertise and for making the journal prompt pages so special. Thanks to Mary Ann and Joseph Coppola for the love and support they gave to displaced children.

About the Author

Lisa "LC" Coppola is a licensed mental health counselor and a domestic adoptee through the Department of Children and Family Services. She is a heartfelt advocate for those relinquished, serves as a therapist, and is the creator of the Voices Unheard: Real Adoptee Stories speaker and writing workshop series in collaboration with Boston Post Adoption Resources (BPAR). Lisa lives in the Boston area and often writes on themes around relinquishment and addiction.

About Boston Post Adoption Resources (BPAR)

Boston Post Adoption Resources, also known as BPAR, is a nonprofit organization that was founded by Jennifer Eckert in 2012 to support all individuals and families who are touched by adoption.

> The BPAR mission is to provide specialized therapeutic support, connect individuals and families to resources, and educate the public about post adoption services to ensure that all those touched by adoption lead healthy, productive lives.
>
> BPAR's team of licensed mental health professionals is specifically trained to deal with post adoption challenges with adoptees of all ages, adoptive parents, and birth parents in individual, family, and group settings. Recognizing that every situation is different, BPAR's goal is to provide support to all in the adoption constellation on their lifelong journey through adoption.

BPAR shares free resources on the BPAR.org website and regularly creates blogs, workshops, and peer training. An illustrated 2017 book, *Adoption Is a Lifelong Journey*, written for adoptive parents in the voice of a young adoptee, is critically acclaimed by twenty adoption experts and has sold thousands of copies.

For more information, please contact Boston Post Adoption Resources, 235 Cypress Street, Suite 310, Brookline, MA 02445 | www.BPAR.org.

Visit BPAR.ORG to access a broad variety of post adoption resources to support the entire adoption constellation.

Made in the USA
Middletown, DE
04 November 2022

13968785R00077